Amara Honeck

CREATIVE MEDITATION®
POSITIVITY AND MANIFESTATION

JOURNAL

3 Month Workbook

Soul Reflections Press LLC

www.AmaraHoneck.com

ISBN 10: 0-9971178-1-8
ISBN 13: 978-0-9971178-1-3

"Creative Meditation" is a registered trademark of
Soul Reflections Press LLC

Published in the United States of America by
Soul Reflections Press LLC

Also By Amara Honeck

Creative Meditation and Manifestation:
Using Your 21 Innate Powers to Create Your Life

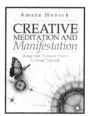

Meditation Coloring Journals:
31 Days of Mindfulness (Series)

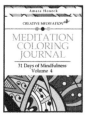 

Thank You ...

For allowing me to be a part of your manifestation journey!

I created this journal as a companion to the book, *Creative Meditation and Manifestation (CMM): Using Your 21 Innate Powers to Create Your Life*. This journal stands on its own to help you achieve real change in your life through positive thought, writing, and interactions.

Journaling is an excellent way to help manifest your goals and is also a form of written meditation. The POWER of Journaling requires you to be present, in the here and now. So when writing, you are mindful and aware of what you are doing. You are in complete control of both your thoughts and the direction your thoughts are taking while you're writing. Manifestation journaling allows you to focus in on manifesting your goals and intentions, shutting down any mind chatter nonsense and negative self talk.

The POWER of Journaling is one of the major POWERS we have because manifestation journaling helps you activate your Creative POWERS every day through positive thought and words. Journaling is such an important part of manifesting your goals, desires, and dreams, starting with the way positive writing has on your ability to change your subconscious belief patterns.

How to Use This Journal

Everything you read about what to include in your manifestation journal in the CMM Power of Journaling chapter has been included on the following pages. You're ready to start! There's no need to fill in all of the sections every day, but do try to write something in your manifestation journal daily so you can be in your creative Power of Journaling and focused on achieving your goals.

Let's Begin!

Journaling about what you want to manifest and bringing those positive emotions to the surface really puts strong energy behind your intentions. Instead of using your journal as a way to express your let downs, disappointments, and negative emotions, let it be a POWER to attract your desires toward you.

Journaling to manifest is a POWERful process because it helps you to focus your mind on what you want and it gives you a chance to write as if the goals have already happened. It also helps keep you in a state of gratitude and positive thought, which is where you want to be as often as possible.

Keep writing, my friend, your manifestation journal not only activates your Creative POWERS, but acts as a record of your manifestation journey. Let your journal writing unfold before you and make it a life changing habit!

Namaste and Much Love,

Positivity and Manifestation Journal

CMM Practice

day _____

Today's Inspirational Quote

Synchronicities and Inspired Actions

Today's Blessing

The Look Back (Date:_____)

Positive
Comment
I Received
Today

Positive
Comment
I Gave
Today

Thank You

Positive
Happenings
Today

Positive
Thoughts
I Had Today

Doodling / Visualization

Positivity and Manifestation Journal

CMM Practice

day_____

Today's Inspirational Quote

Synchronicities and Inspired Actions

Today's Blessing

The Look Back (Date:_____)

Positive
Comment
I Received
Today

Positive
Comment
I Gave
Today

Thank You

Positive
Happenings
Today

Positive
Thoughts
I Had Today

Doodling / Visualization

Positivity and Manifestation Journal

CMM Practice

day _____

Synchronicities and Inspired Actions

Today's Blessing

The Look Back (Date:_____)

Positive
Comment
I Received
Today

Positive
Comment
I Gave
Today

Thank You

Positive
Happenings
Today

Positive
Thoughts
I Had Today

Doodling / Visualization

Positivity and Manifestation Journal

CMM Practice

day_____

Today's Inspirational Quote

Synchronicities and Inspired Actions

Today's Blessing

The Look Back (Date:_____)

Positive
Comment
I Received
Today

Positive
Comment
I Gave
Today

Thank You

Positive
Happenings
Today

Positive
Thoughts
I Had Today

Doodling / Visualization

Positivity and Manifestation Journal

CMM Practice

day_____

Today's Inspirational Quote

Synchronicities and Inspired Actions

Today's Blessing

The Look Back (Date:_____)

Positive
Comment
I Received
Today

Positive
Comment
I Gave
Today

Thank You

Positive
Happenings
Today

Positive
Thoughts
I Had Today

Doodling / Visualization

Positivity and Manifestation Journal

CMM Practice

day _____

Synchronicities and Inspired Actions

Today's Blessing

The Look Back (Date:_____)

Positive
Comment
I Received
Today

Positive
Comment
I Gave
Today

Thank You

Positive
Happenings
Today

Positive
Thoughts
I Had Today

Doodling / Visualization

Positivity and Manifestation Journal

CMM Practice

day_____

Synchronicities and Inspired Actions

Today's Blessing

The Look Back (Date:_____)

Positive
Comment
I Received
Today

Positive
Comment
I Gave
Today

Thank You

Positive
Happenings
Today

Positive
Thoughts
I Had Today

Doodling / Visualization

Positivity and Manifestation Journal

CMM Practice

day_____

Synchronicities and Inspired Actions

Today's Blessing

The Look Back (Date:_____)

Positive
Comment
I Received
Today

Positive
Comment
I Gave
Today

Thank You

Positive
Happenings
Today

Positive
Thoughts
I Had Today

Doodling / Visualization

Positivity and Manifestation Journal

CMM Practice

day _____

Today's Inspirational Quote

"

"

Synchronicities and Inspired Actions

Today's Blessing

The Look Back (Date:_____)

Positive
Comment
I Received
Today

Positive
Comment
I Gave
Today

Thank You

Positive
Happenings
Today

Positive
Thoughts
I Had Today

Doodling / Visualization

Positivity and Manifestation Journal

CMM Practice

day_____

Today's Inspirational Quote

Synchronicities and Inspired Actions

Today's Blessing

The Look Back (Date:_____)

Positive
Comment
I Received
Today

Positive
Comment
I Gave
Today

Thank You

Positive
Happenings
Today

Positive
Thoughts
I Had Today

Doodling / Visualization

Positivity and Manifestation Journal

CMM Practice

day

Synchronicities and Inspired Actions

Today's Blessing

The Look Back (Date:_____)

Positive
Comment
I Received
Today

Positive
Comment
I Gave
Today

Thank You

Positive
Happenings
Today

Positive
Thoughts
I Had Today

Doodling / Visualization

Positivity and Manifestation Journal

CMM Practice

day _____

Synchronicities and Inspired Actions

Today's Blessing

The Look Back (Date:_____)

Positive
Comment
I Received
Today

Positive
Comment
I Gave
Today

Thank You

Positive
Happenings
Today

Positive
Thoughts
I Had Today

Doodling / Visualization

Positivity and Manifestation Journal

CMM Practice

day

Today's Inspirational Quote

Synchronicities and Inspired Actions

Today's Blessing

The Look Back (Date:_____)

Positive
Comment
I Received
Today

Positive
Comment
I Gave
Today

Thank You

Positive
Happenings
Today

Positive
Thoughts
I Had Today

Doodling / Visualization

Positivity and Manifestation Journal

CMM Practice

day_____

Today's Inspirational Quote

Synchronicities and Inspired Actions

Today's Blessing

The Look Back (Date:_____)

Positive
Comment
I Received
Today

Positive
Comment
I Gave
Today

Thank You

Positive
Happenings
Today

Positive
Thoughts
I Had Today

Doodling / Visualization

Positivity and Manifestation Journal

CMM Practice

day _____

Synchronicities and Inspired Actions

Today's Blessing

The Look Back (Date:_____)

Positive
Comment
I Received
Today

Positive
Comment
I Gave
Today

Thank You

Positive
Happenings
Today

Positive
Thoughts
I Had Today

Doodling / Visualization

Positivity and Manifestation Journal

CMM Practice

day_____

Synchronicities and Inspired Actions

Today's Blessing

The Look Back (Date:_____)

Positive
Comment
I Received
Today

Positive
Comment
I Gave
Today

Thank You

Positive
Happenings
Today

Positive
Thoughts
I Had Today

Doodling / Visualization

Positivity and Manifestation Journal

CMM Practice

day

Synchronicities and Inspired Actions

Today's Blessing

The Look Back (Date:_____)

Positive
Comment
I Received
Today

Positive
Comment
I Gave
Today

Thank You

Positive
Happenings
Today

Positive
Thoughts
I Had Today

Doodling / Visualization

Positivity and Manifestation Journal

CMM Practice

day

Synchronicities and Inspired Actions

Today's Blessing

The Look Back (Date:_____)

Positive
Comment
I Received
Today

Positive
Comment
I Gave
Today

Thank You

Positive
Happenings
Today

Positive
Thoughts
I Had Today

Doodling / Visualization

Positivity and Manifestation Journal

CMM Practice

day _____

Synchronicities and Inspired Actions

Today's Blessing

The Look Back (Date:_____)

Positive
Comment
I Received
Today

Positive
Comment
I Gave
Today

Thank You

Positive
Happenings
Today

Positive
Thoughts
I Had Today

Doodling / Visualization

Positivity and Manifestation Journal

CMM Practice

day_____

Synchronicities and Inspired Actions

Today's Blessing

The Look Back (Date:_____)

Positive
Comment
I Received
Today

Positive
Comment
I Gave
Today

Thank You

Positive
Happenings
Today

Positive
Thoughts
I Had Today

Doodling / Visualization

Positivity and Manifestation Journal

CMM Practice

day _____

Today's Inspirational Quote

Synchronicities and Inspired Actions

Today's Blessing

The Look Back (Date:_____)

Positive
Comment
I Received
Today

Positive
Comment
I Gave
Today

Thank You

Positive
Happenings
Today

Positive
Thoughts
I Had Today

Doodling / Visualization

Positivity and Manifestation Journal

CMM Practice

day_____

Today's Inspirational Quote

Synchronicities and Inspired Actions

Today's Blessing

The Look Back (Date:_____)

Positive
Comment
I Received
Today

Positive
Comment
I Gave
Today

Thank You

Positive
Happenings
Today

Positive
Thoughts
I Had Today

Doodling / Visualization

Positivity and Manifestation Journal

CMM Practice

day_____

Synchronicities and Inspired Actions

Today's Blessing

The Look Back (Date:_____)

Positive
Comment
I Received
Today

Positive
Comment
I Gave
Today

Thank You

Positive
Happenings
Today

Positive
Thoughts
I Had Today

Doodling / Visualization

Positivity and Manifestation Journal

CMM Practice

day _____

Synchronicities and Inspired Actions

Today's Blessing

The Look Back (Date:_____)

Positive
Comment
I Received
Today

Positive
Comment
I Gave
Today

Thank You

Positive
Happenings
Today

Positive
Thoughts
I Had Today

Doodling / Visualization

Positivity and Manifestation Journal

CMM Practice

day_____

Today's Inspirational Quote

Synchronicities and Inspired Actions

Today's Blessing

The Look Back (Date:_____)

Positive
Comment
I Received
Today

Positive
Comment
I Gave
Today

Thank You

Positive
Happenings
Today

Positive
Thoughts
I Had Today

Doodling / Visualization

Positivity and Manifestation Journal

CMM Practice

day_____

Synchronicities and Inspired Actions

Today's Blessing

The Look Back (Date:_____)

Positive
Comment
I Received
Today

Positive
Comment
I Gave
Today

Thank You

Positive
Happenings
Today

Positive
Thoughts
I Had Today

Doodling / Visualization

Positivity and Manifestation Journal

CMM Practice

" Today's Inspirational Quote "

Synchronicities and Inspired Actions

Today's Blessing

The Look Back (Date:_____)

Positive
Comment
I Received
Today

Positive
Comment
I Gave
Today

Thank You

Positive
Happenings
Today

Positive
Thoughts
I Had Today

Doodling / Visualization

Positivity and Manifestation Journal

CMM Practice

day_____

Today's Inspirational Quote

Synchronicities and Inspired Actions

Today's Blessing

The Look Back (Date:_____)

Positive
Comment
I Received
Today

Positive
Comment
I Gave
Today

Thank You

Positive
Happenings
Today

Positive
Thoughts
I Had Today

Doodling / Visualization

Positivity and Manifestation Journal

CMM Practice

Today's Inspirational Quote

Synchronicities and Inspired Actions

Today's Blessing

The Look Back (Date:_____)

Positive
Comment
I Received
Today

Positive
Comment
I Gave
Today

Thank You

Positive
Happenings
Today

Positive
Thoughts
I Had Today

Doodling / Visualization

Positivity and Manifestation Journal

CMM Practice

day

Synchronicities and Inspired Actions

Today's Blessing

The Look Back (Date:_____)

Positive
Comment
I Received
Today

Positive
Comment
I Gave
Today

Thank You

Positive
Happenings
Today

Positive
Thoughts
I Had Today

Doodling / Visualization

Positivity and Manifestation Journal

CMM Practice

day _____

Synchronicities and Inspired Actions

Today's Blessing

The Look Back (Date:_____)

Positive
Comment
I Received
Today

Positive
Comment
I Gave
Today

Thank You

Positive
Happenings
Today

Positive
Thoughts
I Had Today

Doodling / Visualization

Positivity and Manifestation Journal

CMM Practice

Today's Inspirational Quote

Synchronicities and Inspired Actions

Today's Blessing

The Look Back (Date:_____)

Positive
Comment
I Received
Today

Positive
Comment
I Gave
Today

Thank You

Positive
Happenings
Today

Positive
Thoughts
I Had Today

Doodling / Visualization

Positivity and Manifestation Journal

CMM Practice

Today's Inspirational Quote

Synchronicities and Inspired Actions

Today's Blessing

The Look Back (Date:_____)

Positive
Comment
I Received
Today

Positive
Comment
I Gave
Today

Thank You

Positive
Happenings
Today

Positive
Thoughts
I Had Today

Doodling / Visualization

Positivity and Manifestation Journal

CMM Practice

day_____

Today's Inspirational Quote

Synchronicities and Inspired Actions

Today's Blessing

The Look Back (Date:_____)

Positive
Comment
I Received
Today

Positive
Comment
I Gave
Today

Thank You

Positive
Happenings
Today

Positive
Thoughts
I Had Today

Doodling / Visualization

Positivity and Manifestation Journal

CMM Practice

day_____

Synchronicities and Inspired Actions

Today's Blessing

The Look Back (Date:_____)

Positive
Comment
I Received
Today

Positive
Comment
I Gave
Today

Thank You

Positive
Happenings
Today

Positive
Thoughts
I Had Today

Doodling / Visualization

Positivity and Manifestation Journal

CMM Practice

day_____

Today's Inspirational Quote

Synchronicities and Inspired Actions

Today's Blessing

The Look Back (Date:_____)

Positive
Comment
I Received
Today

Positive
Comment
I Gave
Today

Thank You

Positive
Happenings
Today

Positive
Thoughts
I Had Today

Doodling / Visualization

Positivity and Manifestation Journal

CMM Practice

day _____

" "

Today's Inspirational Quote

Synchronicities and Inspired Actions

Today's Blessing

The Look Back (Date:_____)

Positive
Comment
I Received
Today

Positive
Comment
I Gave
Today

Thank You

Positive
Happenings
Today

Positive
Thoughts
I Had Today

Doodling / Visualization

Positivity and Manifestation Journal

CMM Practice

day

Synchronicities and Inspired Actions

Today's Blessing

The Look Back (Date:_____)

Positive
Comment
I Received
Today

Positive
Comment
I Gave
Today

Thank You

Positive
Happenings
Today

Positive
Thoughts
I Had Today

Doodling / Visualization

Positivity and Manifestation Journal

CMM Practice

day_____

Synchronicities and Inspired Actions

Today's Blessing

The Look Back (Date:_____)

Positive
Comment
I Received
Today

Positive
Comment
I Gave
Today

Thank You

Positive
Happenings
Today

Positive
Thoughts
I Had Today

Doodling / Visualization

Positivity and Manifestation Journal

CMM Practice

day _____

Today's Inspirational Quote

Synchronicities and Inspired Actions

Today's Blessing

The Look Back (Date:_____)

Positive
Comment
I Received
Today

Positive
Comment
I Gave
Today

Thank You

Positive
Happenings
Today

Positive
Thoughts
I Had Today

Doodling / Visualization

Positivity and Manifestation Journal

CMM Practice

day

Synchronicities and Inspired Actions

Today's Blessing

The Look Back (Date:_____)

Positive
Comment
I Received
Today

Positive
Comment
I Gave
Today

Thank You

Positive
Happenings
Today

Positive
Thoughts
I Had Today

Doodling / Visualization

Positivity and Manifestation Journal

CMM Practice

day_____

Synchronicities and Inspired Actions

Today's Blessing

The Look Back (Date:_____)

Positive
Comment
I Received
Today

Positive
Comment
I Gave
Today

Thank You

Positive
Happenings
Today

Positive
Thoughts
I Had Today

Doodling / Visualization

Positivity and Manifestation Journal

CMM Practice

day_____

Synchronicities and Inspired Actions

Today's Blessing

The Look Back (Date:_____)

Positive
Comment
I Received
Today

Positive
Comment
I Gave
Today

Thank You

Positive
Happenings
Today

Positive
Thoughts
I Had Today

Doodling / Visualization

Positivity and Manifestation Journal

CMM Practice

day _____

Today's Inspirational Quote

....
....
....
....
....

....
....
....
....
....
....
....
....
....
....
....
....
....
....
....
....
....
....
....
....
....
....
....
....
....

Synchronicities and Inspired Actions

Today's Blessing

The Look Back (Date:_____)

Positive
Comment
I Received
Today

Positive
Comment
I Gave
Today

Thank You

Positive
Happenings
Today

Positive
Thoughts
I Had Today

Doodling / Visualization

Positivity and Manifestation Journal

CMM Practice

day_____

Today's Inspirational Quote

Synchronicities and Inspired Actions

Today's Blessing

The Look Back (Date:_____)

Positive
Comment
I Received
Today

Positive
Comment
I Gave
Today

Thank You

Positive
Happenings
Today

Positive
Thoughts
I Had Today

Doodling / Visualization

Positivity and Manifestation Journal

CMM Practice

day

Today's Inspirational Quote

Synchronicities and Inspired Actions

Today's Blessing

The Look Back (Date:_____)

Positive
Comment
I Received
Today

Positive
Comment
I Gave
Today

Thank You

Positive
Happenings
Today

Positive
Thoughts
I Had Today

Doodling / Visualization

Positivity and Manifestation Journal

CMM Practice

Today's Inspirational Quote

Synchronicities and Inspired Actions

Today's Blessing

The Look Back (Date:_____)

Positive
Comment
I Received
Today

Positive
Comment
I Gave
Today

Thank You

Positive
Happenings
Today

Positive
Thoughts
I Had Today

Doodling / Visualization

Positivity and Manifestation Journal

CMM Practice

day_____

Synchronicities and Inspired Actions

Today's Blessing

The Look Back (Date:_____)

Positive
Comment
I Received
Today

Positive
Comment
I Gave
Today

Thank You

Positive
Happenings
Today

Positive
Thoughts
I Had Today

Doodling / Visualization

Positivity and Manifestation Journal

CMM Practice

day_____

Synchronicities and Inspired Actions

Today's Blessing

The Look Back (Date:_____)

Positive
Comment
I Received
Today

Positive
Comment
I Gave
Today

Thank You

Positive
Happenings
Today

Positive
Thoughts
I Had Today

Doodling / Visualization

Positivity and Manifestation Journal

CMM Practice

day_____

Today's Inspirational Quote

Synchronicities and Inspired Actions

Today's Blessing

The Look Back (Date:_____)

Positive
Comment
I Received
Today

Positive
Comment
I Gave
Today

Thank You

Positive
Happenings
Today

Positive
Thoughts
I Had Today

Doodling / Visualization

Positivity and Manifestation Journal

CMM Practice

day _____

Synchronicities and Inspired Actions

Today's Blessing

The Look Back (Date:_____)

Positive
Comment
I Received
Today

Positive
Comment
I Gave
Today

Thank You

Positive
Happenings
Today

Positive
Thoughts
I Had Today

Doodling / Visualization

Positivity and Manifestation Journal

CMM Practice

day_____

Today's Inspirational Quote

Synchronicities and Inspired Actions

Today's Blessing

The Look Back (Date:_____)

Positive
Comment
I Received
Today

Positive
Comment
I Gave
Today

Thank You

Positive
Happenings
Today

Positive
Thoughts
I Had Today

Doodling / Visualization

Positivity and Manifestation Journal

CMM Practice

day_____

Today's Inspirational Quote

Synchronicities and Inspired Actions

Today's Blessing

The Look Back (Date:_____)

Positive
Comment
I Received
Today

Positive
Comment
I Gave
Today

Thank You

Positive
Happenings
Today

Positive
Thoughts
I Had Today

Doodling / Visualization

Positivity and Manifestation Journal

CMM Practice

day

Today's Inspirational Quote

Synchronicities and Inspired Actions

Today's Blessing

The Look Back (Date:_____)

Positive
Comment
I Received
Today

Positive
Comment
I Gave
Today

Thank You

Positive
Happenings
Today

Positive
Thoughts
I Had Today

Doodling / Visualization

Positivity and Manifestation Journal

CMM Practice

day _____

Today's Inspirational Quote

Synchronicities and Inspired Actions

Today's Blessing

The Look Back (Date:_____)

Positive Comment I Received Today

Positive Comment I Gave Today

Thank You

Positive Happenings Today

Positive Thoughts I Had Today

Doodling / Visualization

Positivity and Manifestation Journal

CMM Practice

day

Today's Inspirational Quote

Synchronicities and Inspired Actions

Today's Blessing

The Look Back (Date:_____)

Positive
Comment
I Received
Today

Positive
Comment
I Gave
Today

Thank You

Positive
Happenings
Today

Positive
Thoughts
I Had Today

Doodling / Visualization

Positivity and Manifestation Journal

CMM Practice

day_____

Today's Inspirational Quote

Synchronicities and Inspired Actions

Today's Blessing

The Look Back (Date:_____)

Positive
Comment
I Received
Today

Positive
Comment
I Gave
Today

Thank You

Positive
Happenings
Today

Positive
Thoughts
I Had Today

Doodling / Visualization

Positivity and Manifestation Journal

CMM Practice

day_____

Today's Inspirational Quote

Synchronicities and Inspired Actions

Today's Blessing

The Look Back (Date:_____)

Positive
Comment
I Received
Today

Positive
Comment
I Gave
Today

Thank You

Positive
Happenings
Today

Positive
Thoughts
I Had Today

Doodling / Visualization

Positivity and Manifestation Journal

CMM Practice

Today's Inspirational Quote

Synchronicities and Inspired Actions

Today's Blessing

The Look Back (Date:_____)

Positive
Comment
I Received
Today

Positive
Comment
I Gave
Today

Thank You

Positive
Happenings
Today

Positive
Thoughts
I Had Today

Doodling / Visualization

Positivity and Manifestation Journal

CMM Practice

day_____

Today's Inspirational Quote

Synchronicities and Inspired Actions

Today's Blessing

The Look Back (Date:_____)

Positive
Comment
I Received
Today

Positive
Comment
I Gave
Today

Thank You

Positive
Happenings
Today

Positive
Thoughts
I Had Today

Doodling / Visualization

Positivity and Manifestation Journal

CMM Practice

day _____

Today's Inspirational Quote

Synchronicities and Inspired Actions

Today's Blessing

The Look Back (Date:_____)

Positive
Comment
I Received
Today

Positive
Comment
I Gave
Today

Thank You

Positive
Happenings
Today

Positive
Thoughts
I Had Today

Doodling / Visualization

Positivity and Manifestation Journal

CMM Practice

day _____

Synchronicities and Inspired Actions

Today's Blessing

The Look Back (Date:_____)

Positive
Comment
I Received
Today

Positive
Comment
I Gave
Today

Thank You

Positive
Happenings
Today

Positive
Thoughts
I Had Today

Doodling / Visualization

Positivity and Manifestation Journal

CMM Practice

day_____

Today's Inspirational Quote

Synchronicities and Inspired Actions

Today's Blessing

The Look Back (Date:_____)

Positive
Comment
I Received
Today

Positive
Comment
I Gave
Today

Thank You

Positive
Happenings
Today

Positive
Thoughts
I Had Today

Doodling / Visualization

Positivity and Manifestation Journal

CMM Practice

day_____

" Today's Inspirational Quote

Synchronicities and Inspired Actions

Today's Blessing

The Look Back (Date:_____)

Positive
Comment
I Received
Today

Positive
Comment
I Gave
Today

Thank You

Positive
Happenings
Today

Positive
Thoughts
I Had Today

Doodling / Visualization

Positivity and Manifestation Journal

CMM Practice

day _____

Synchronicities and Inspired Actions

Today's Blessing

The Look Back (Date:_____)

Positive
Comment
I Received
Today

Positive
Comment
I Gave
Today

Thank You

Positive
Happenings
Today

Positive
Thoughts
I Had Today

Doodling / Visualization

Positivity and Manifestation Journal

CMM Practice

day _____

Synchronicities and Inspired Actions

Today's Blessing

The Look Back (Date:_____)

Positive
Comment
I Received
Today

Positive
Comment
I Gave
Today

Thank You

Positive
Happenings
Today

Positive
Thoughts
I Had Today

Doodling / Visualization

Positivity and Manifestation Journal

CMM Practice

Today's Inspirational Quote

Synchronicities and Inspired Actions

Today's Blessing

The Look Back (Date:_____)

Positive
Comment
I Received
Today

Positive
Comment
I Gave
Today

Thank You

Positive
Happenings
Today

Positive
Thoughts
I Had Today

Doodling / Visualization

Positivity and Manifestation Journal

CMM Practice

Today's Inspirational Quote

Synchronicities and Inspired Actions

Today's Blessing

The Look Back (Date:_____)

Positive
Comment
I Received
Today

Positive
Comment
I Gave
Today

Thank You

Positive
Happenings
Today

Positive
Thoughts
I Had Today

Doodling / Visualization

Positivity and Manifestation Journal

CMM Practice

day_____

Today's Inspirational Quote

Synchronicities and Inspired Actions

Today's Blessing

The Look Back (Date:_____)

Positive
Comment
I Received
Today

Positive
Comment
I Gave
Today

Thank You

Positive
Happenings
Today

Positive
Thoughts
I Had Today

Doodling / Visualization

Positivity and Manifestation Journal

CMM Practice

day_____

Today's Inspirational Quote

Synchronicities and Inspired Actions

Today's Blessing

The Look Back (Date:_____)

Positive
Comment
I Received
Today

Positive
Comment
I Gave
Today

Thank You

Positive
Happenings
Today

Positive
Thoughts
I Had Today

Doodling / Visualization

Positivity and Manifestation Journal

CMM Practice

day

Today's Inspirational Quote

Synchronicities and Inspired Actions

Today's Blessing

The Look Back (Date:_____)

Positive
Comment
I Received
Today

Positive
Comment
I Gave
Today

Thank You

Positive
Happenings
Today

Positive
Thoughts
I Had Today

Doodling / Visualization

Positivity and Manifestation Journal

CMM Practice

day

Synchronicities and Inspired Actions

Today's Blessing

The Look Back (Date:_____)

Positive
Comment
I Received
Today

Positive
Comment
I Gave
Today

Thank You

Positive
Happenings
Today

Positive
Thoughts
I Had Today

Doodling / Visualization

Positivity and Manifestation Journal

CMM Practice

day_____

Today's Inspirational Quote

Synchronicities and Inspired Actions

Today's Blessing

The Look Back (Date:_____)

Positive
Comment
I Received
Today

Positive
Comment
I Gave
Today

Thank You

Positive
Happenings
Today

Positive
Thoughts
I Had Today

Doodling / Visualization

Positivity and Manifestation Journal

CMM Practice

Today's Inspirational Quote

Synchronicities and Inspired Actions

Today's Blessing

The Look Back (Date:_____)

Positive
Comment
I Received
Today

Positive
Comment
I Gave
Today

Thank You

Positive
Happenings
Today

Positive
Thoughts
I Had Today

Doodling / Visualization

Positivity and Manifestation Journal

CMM Practice

Today's Inspirational Quote

Synchronicities and Inspired Actions

Today's Blessing

The Look Back (Date:_____)

Positive
Comment
I Received
Today

Positive
Comment
I Gave
Today

Thank You

Positive
Happenings
Today

Positive
Thoughts
I Had Today

Doodling / Visualization

Positivity and Manifestation Journal

CMM Practice

day_____

Today's Inspirational Quote

Synchronicities and Inspired Actions

Today's Blessing

The Look Back (Date:_____)

Positive
Comment
I Received
Today

Positive
Comment
I Gave
Today

Thank You

Positive
Happenings
Today

Positive
Thoughts
I Had Today

Doodling / Visualization

Positivity and Manifestation Journal

CMM Practice

Today's Inspirational Quote

Synchronicities and Inspired Actions

Today's Blessing

The Look Back (Date:_____)

Positive
Comment
I Received
Today

Positive
Comment
I Gave
Today

Thank You

Positive
Happenings
Today

Positive
Thoughts
I Had Today

Doodling / Visualization

Positivity and Manifestation Journal

CMM Practice

Today's Inspirational Quote

Synchronicities and Inspired Actions

Today's Blessing

The Look Back (Date:_____)

Positive
Comment
I Received
Today

Positive
Comment
I Gave
Today

Thank You

Positive
Happenings
Today

Positive
Thoughts
I Had Today

Doodling / Visualization

Positivity and Manifestation Journal

CMM Practice

day

Today's Inspirational Quote

Synchronicities and Inspired Actions

Today's Blessing

The Look Back (Date:_____)

Positive
Comment
I Received
Today

Positive
Comment
I Gave
Today

Thank You

Positive
Happenings
Today

Positive
Thoughts
I Had Today

Doodling / Visualization

Positivity and Manifestation Journal

CMM Practice

Today's Inspirational Quote

Synchronicities and Inspired Actions

Today's Blessing

The Look Back (Date:_____)

Positive
Comment
I Received
Today

Positive
Comment
I Gave
Today

Thank You

Positive
Happenings
Today

Positive
Thoughts
I Had Today

Doodling / Visualization

Positivity and Manifestation Journal

CMM Practice

Today's Inspirational Quote

Synchronicities and Inspired Actions

Today's Blessing

The Look Back (Date:_____)

Positive
Comment
I Received
Today

Positive
Comment
I Gave
Today

Thank You

Positive
Happenings
Today

Positive
Thoughts
I Had Today

Doodling / Visualization

Positivity and Manifestation Journal

CMM Practice

day_____

" Today's Inspirational Quote

Synchronicities and Inspired Actions

Today's Blessing

The Look Back (Date:_____)

Positive
Comment
I Received
Today

Positive
Comment
I Gave
Today

Thank You

Positive
Happenings
Today

Positive
Thoughts
I Had Today

Doodling / Visualization

Positivity and Manifestation Journal

CMM Practice

day_____

Synchronicities and Inspired Actions

Today's Blessing

The Look Back (Date:_____)

Positive
Comment
I Received
Today

Positive
Comment
I Gave
Today

Thank You

Positive
Happenings
Today

Positive
Thoughts
I Had Today

Doodling / Visualization

Positivity and Manifestation Journal

CMM Practice

Today's Inspirational Quote

Synchronicities and Inspired Actions

Today's Blessing

The Look Back (Date:_____)

Positive
Comment
I Received
Today

Positive
Comment
I Gave
Today

Thank You

Positive
Happenings
Today

Positive
Thoughts
I Had Today

Doodling / Visualization

Positivity and Manifestation Journal

CMM Practice

day _____

Synchronicities and Inspired Actions

Today's Blessing

The Look Back (Date:_____)

Positive
Comment
I Received
Today

Positive
Comment
I Gave
Today

Thank You

Positive
Happenings
Today

Positive
Thoughts
I Had Today

Doodling / Visualization

Positivity and Manifestation Journal

CMM Practice

day_____

Synchronicities and Inspired Actions

Today's Blessing

The Look Back (Date:_____)

Positive
Comment
I Received
Today

Positive
Comment
I Gave
Today

Thank You

Positive
Happenings
Today

Positive
Thoughts
I Had Today

Doodling / Visualization

Positivity and Manifestation Journal

CMM Practice

day_____

Synchronicities and Inspired Actions

Today's Blessing

The Look Back (Date:_____)

Positive
Comment
I Received
Today

Positive
Comment
I Gave
Today

Thank You

Positive
Happenings
Today

Positive
Thoughts
I Had Today

Doodling / Visualization

Positivity and Manifestation Journal

CMM Practice

day_____

Today's Inspirational Quote

Synchronicities and Inspired Actions

Today's Blessing

The Look Back (Date:_____)

Positive
Comment
I Received
Today

Positive
Comment
I Gave
Today

Thank You

Positive
Happenings
Today

Positive
Thoughts
I Had Today

Doodling / Visualization

Positivity and Manifestation Journal

CMM Practice

day_____

Today's Inspirational Quote

"

"

Synchronicities and Inspired Actions

Today's Blessing

The Look Back (Date:_____)

Positive
Comment
I Received
Today

Positive
Comment
I Gave
Today

Thank You

Positive
Happenings
Today

Positive
Thoughts
I Had Today

Doodling / Visualization

Positivity and Manifestation Journal

CMM Practice

day _____

Synchronicities and Inspired Actions

Today's Blessing

Positive
Comment
I Received
Today

The Look Back (Date:_____)

Positive
Comment
I Gave
Today

Thank You

Positive
Happenings
Today

Positive
Thoughts
I Had Today

Doodling / Visualization

Positivity and Manifestation Journal

CMM Practice

day _____

Synchronicities and Inspired Actions

Today's Blessing

The Look Back (Date:_____)

Positive Comment I Received Today

Positive Comment I Gave Today

Thank You

Positive Happenings Today

Positive Thoughts I Had Today

Doodling / Visualization

Positivity and Manifestation Journal

CMM Practice

day

Synchronicities and Inspired Actions

Today's Blessing

The Look Back (Date:_____)

Positive
Comment
I Received
Today

Positive
Comment
I Gave
Today

Thank You

Positive
Happenings
Today

Positive
Thoughts
I Had Today

Doodling / Visualization

Positivity and Manifestation Journal

CMM Practice

day_____

Today's Inspirational Quote

Synchronicities and Inspired Actions

Today's Blessing

The Look Back (Date:_____)

Positive
Comment
I Received
Today

Positive
Comment
I Gave
Today

Thank You

Positive
Happenings
Today

Positive
Thoughts
I Had Today

Doodling / Visualization

Made in the USA
Middletown, DE
27 December 2022

17878134R00110